Starry Science

Lynn Huggins-Cooper

Wizard Whimstaff lives in a faraway land, in a magical cave. He searches for apprentices so he can pass on his powerful Science spells. This time Wizard Whimstaff has chosen you!

He has a goblin helper called Pointy, who is very clever. Pointy helps Wizard Whimstaff keep his spell books tidy. He also stirs the smelly cauldron to make scientific words appear.

Pointy has two pet frogs called Mugly and Bugly. They are very lazy. They spend most of their time eating, burping and sleeping. Their friend Miss Snufflebeam also lives in the cave. She is a little dragon. She cannot breathe fire yet, so puffs small clouds of smoke instead!

Wizard Whimstaff and his friends are very happy, solving Science problems. Join them on a magical quest to win the Trophy of Science Wizardry!

Contents

Great Growing

Hello! My name is Wizard Whimstaff!
My magic can help you to learn about
science! Have you seen pictures of yourself
as a **baby** and **toddler**? Did you look very
different? We all change as we **grow**!
Look at these pictures of me!

aged 2   aged 13

Task 1 Look at these photos of Miss Snufflebeam, a little dragon
friend. She is bigger now, but she started off very small! Can
you put her photos in the right order?

a  b  c  d  e

Task 2 Mugly and Bugly, the two lazy frogs, have changed even
more than Miss Snufflebeam! Can you put their photos in
the right order? Hey presto!

a  b 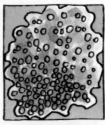 c 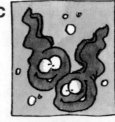 d  e

Task 3 Excellent work! Now see if you can match the mums and babies correctly. Join them with a line.

a

b

c

d

e

f

g

h

1

2

3

4

5

6

7

8

Sorcerer's Skill Check

True or false? Put **T** for true and **F** for false. Abracadabra!

a Humans change completely as they grow, just like a frog.

b Human babies look like their parents, but smaller.

c Tadpoles grow up to be chickens.

d Tadpoles grow up to be frogs.

e Kittens look like their parents, only smaller.

f Butterflies grow up to be caterpillars.

Super work! Put your first silver shield
on the trophy at the back of your book!

Fantastic Food

I'm Pointy and I like to prepare healthy food for Wizard Whimstaff. We eat lots of fruit and vegetables, and we drink milk and orange juice. It is our healthy diet that keeps us fit and well. Wizards need to keep their strength up, so we do lots of exercise, too!

Task 1 I am preparing some menus for lunches. Choose the healthier meal from each pair by drawing a line under it.

a Burger and chips or cheese omelette?

b Baked potato and beans or fried bacon sandwich?

c Fish and chips or pasta with tomato sauce?

d Egg salad sandwich or take away pizza?

Task 2 I need your help to plan Miss Snufflebeam's lunch. Draw a healthy meal in her lunchbox. Use the food in the box below to help you.

Task 3 Read the sentences I have written to remind myself to do healthy things. Naughty Mugly and Bugly have scribbled silly things on it that are not at all healthy! Cross out the things that are not healthy.

eat lots of fruit eat bags and bags of sweets

go swimming

lie about in front of the TV all day

eat lots of vegetables stay up late every night

only drink fizzy lemonade play football

drink lots of water get plenty of sleep

Sorcerer's Skill Check

Just to check that you have remembered everything, answer these questions. Write **T** for true and **F** for false. It is easy when you know how!

a Cheese, eggs and milk are good foods for growing children.

b We should eat 6 bags of sweets every day to stay healthy.

c We need to eat lots of fruit and vegetables.

d Staying up late every night is good for you.

e We should only drink fizzy orange.

f Never brush your teeth as it will damage them.

Well done! I do not think I could have answered those questions. Give yourself a silver shield!

Mighty Medicine

I am Miss Snufflebeam and sometimes I get things muddled. I had to take some medicine the other day, because I had a nasty cough. Wizard Whimstaff said there were rules to follow to make sure you stay safe with medicine.

1. Never take medicine unless a grown-up gives it to you.
2. Never take things from the medicine cabinet.
3. Do not take more medicine than the bottle tells you to.
4. Be careful because pills can look like sweets!

Task 1 I am worried that I will forget the rules very quickly! Draw a poster to remind me to be careful with medicines and pills.

Task 2 Wizard Whimstaff told me a story about Silly Sally to see if I could remember to be safe around medicines. Help me by drawing a line underneath the silly things Sally does in this story.

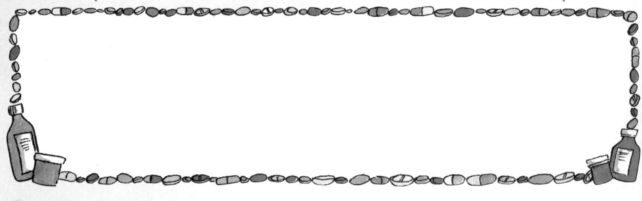

Silly Sally had a bad headache. She went into the bathroom and opened the medicine cupboard. She took out a bottle of medicine she had seen her mum use. Just then, Mum came into the bathroom. 'Put that down, Sally!' said Mum. 'Children must not help themselves to medicine. It can be very dangerous!' Sally asked her mum to give her lots of medicine because she had a headache. Her mum said 'No, silly! You must only take one spoonful, like it says on the bottle.'

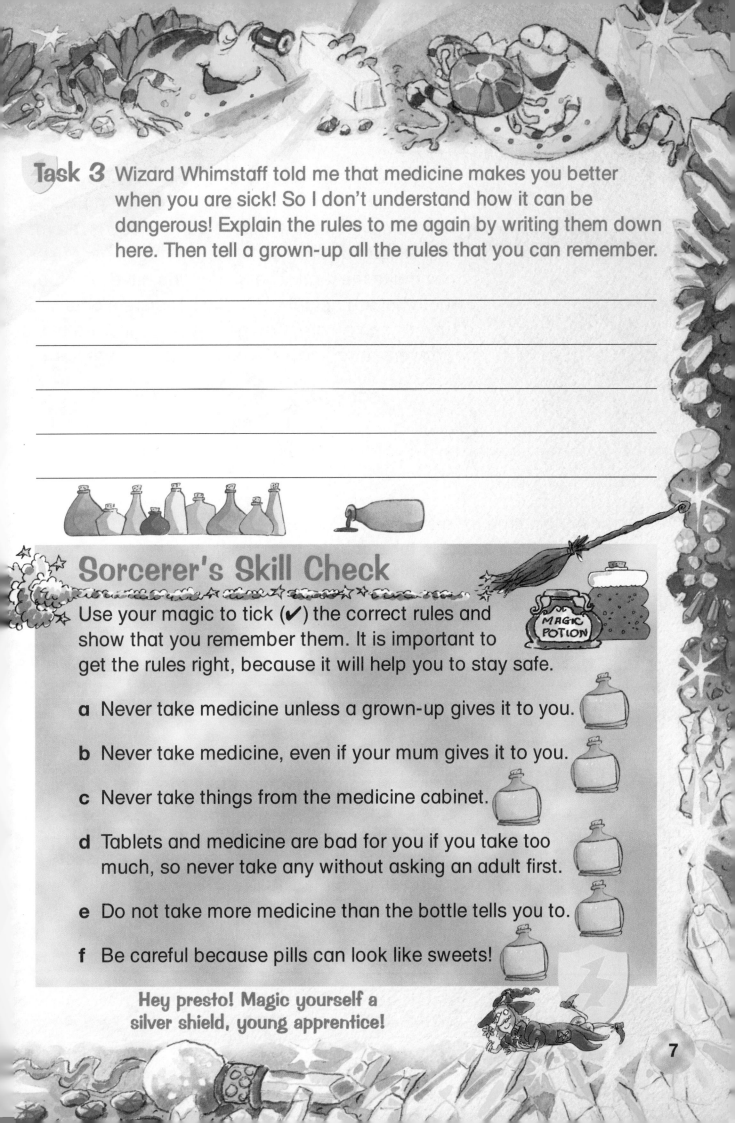

Task 3 Wizard Whimstaff told me that medicine makes you better when you are sick! So I don't understand how it can be dangerous! Explain the rules to me again by writing them down here. Then tell a grown-up all the rules that you can remember.

Sorcerer's Skill Check

Use your magic to tick (✔) the correct rules and show that you remember them. It is important to get the rules right, because it will help you to stay safe.

a Never take medicine unless a grown-up gives it to you.

b Never take medicine, even if your mum gives it to you.

c Never take things from the medicine cabinet.

d Tablets and medicine are bad for you if you take too much, so never take any without asking an adult first.

e Do not take more medicine than the bottle tells you to.

f Be careful because pills can look like sweets!

Hey presto! Magic yourself a silver shield, young apprentice!

Potty Plants

Hello, we are Mugly and Bugly. We love plants, because juicy bugs live on them! Plants have lots of different parts – leaves, stem, roots and flowers. We like leaves best, because they make the food! The other parts have jobs too. Roots hold the plant in the soil. The stem acts like a tube to carry water and goodness round the plant. Flowers attract insects, so we like flowers, too!

Task 1 Is it time for a snooze yet? No? Well, try this quick quiz. Put the labels in the right place on the flower.

leaf   stem   roots   flower

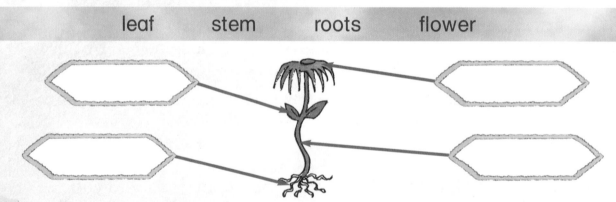

Task 2 Croak! Now draw the part of the plant that the label describes.

a makes food for the plant

b holds the plant in the soil

c carries water and goodness around the plant

d attracts insects

Task 3 You know we love eating! But can you match these animals with the food they eat? It's amazing, they all eat plant parts! Match the animals to their food with a line.

I love this crunchy root!

Yum! I munch leaves.

I eat fruit slices.

This flower is delicious!

Stems are my favourite.

a
b
c
d
e

a lettuce is a leaf

a carrot is a root

a rose is a flower

celery is a stem

an apple is a fruit

Sorcerer's Skill Check

Brain cell alert! See if you can remember everything! Draw a picture of a plant in this box, then add the labels yourself!

Super! You deserve a silver shield for helping my pet frogs!

Seed Sorcery

When tiny seeds start to sprout and then grow, it seems like magic! Seeds need water and warmth to sprout. As plants grow bigger, they also need light. The light from the sun is used by the leaves to make food for the plant.

These seeds are just starting to sprout.

Task 1 Miss Snufflebeam is very excited, as she is growing flowers! She has drawn some pictures of them growing. Can you put the pots in the right order?

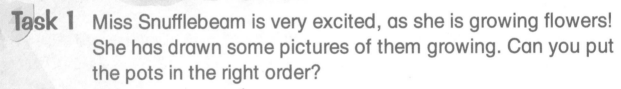

a   b   c   d

Task 2 Miss Snufflebeam is very forgetful. Put these instructions in the right order, so she can remember what to do the next time she plants seeds. Abracadabra!

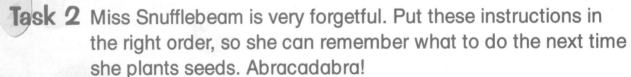

a	b	c	d
Put the pot in a warm place.	Put compost in a pot.	Water the seed.	Put the seed in the pot and cover it with compost.

Task 3 Some plants can catch flies! Mugly and Bugly think they will help them to catch their dinner so they planted some seeds! Draw pictures to show what they did.

a We collected some stinky mud and put it in a pot.

b We planted a seed in the yummy mud.

c Then we slopped some pond water on the seed.

d We put the seed somewhere warm (yuck!)

e It started to grow!

Sorcerer's Skill Check

Allakazan! Here's a quiz to check if you have remembered everything. Tick (✔) the sentences that tell the truth.

a Seeds need to be dry to sprout.

b Seeds need water to make them grow.

c Plants need sunlight.

d Plants need to be in the dark.

e Plants need to be kept in the freezer.

Slurp! That seemed like hard work! Give yourself a silver shield, then have a snooze!

11

Playful Pets

Wizard Whimstaff has let me have a pet rat! I have called her Rizzo. She has a big cage, with toys inside. I feed her a variety of food and give her fresh water every day. She has soft hay to make a bed in. I play with her all the time, because I love her and I do not want her to get bored.

water
toys
soft hay
food

Task 1 I must be organised to look after Rizzo properly! Fill in the gaps using the words in the box below.

water	play	food	clean	toys

a Rizzo needs her cage to be kept __ __ __ __ __ .

b I must give her fresh __ __ __ __ __ every day.

c I must __ __ __ __ with Rizzo so she doesn't get bored!

d Rizzo needs __ __ __ __ to play with.

e Give Rizzo tasty __ __ __ __ every day.

Task 2 Here is a picture of Rizzo in her cage. Draw all the things she needs in her cage to be healthy and happy.

Task 3 Sometimes Miss Snufflebeam looks after Rizzo, but she is forgetful. Make some cards to remind her what to do. Draw a picture and write a sentence. Practice makes perfect!

play

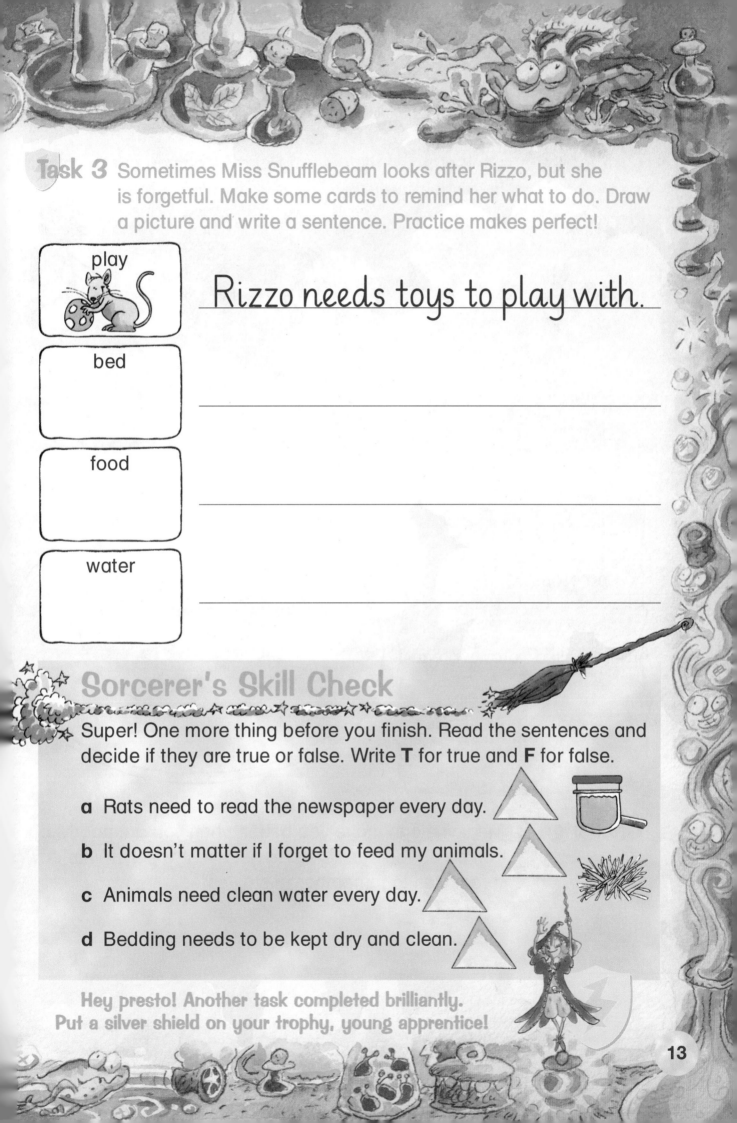

Rizzo needs toys to play with.

bed

_____

food

_____

water

_____

Sorcerer's Skill Check

Super! One more thing before you finish. Read the sentences and decide if they are true or false. Write **T** for true and **F** for false.

a Rats need to read the newspaper every day.

b It doesn't matter if I forget to feed my animals.

c Animals need clean water every day.

d Bedding needs to be kept dry and clean.

Hey presto! Another task completed brilliantly. Put a silver shield on your trophy, young apprentice!

Apprentice Wizard Challenge 1

Challenge 1 Look at these pictures of Pointy. Can you put the pictures in the right order?

a  b  c  d  e

Challenge 2 Choose a healthy meal from the food in the box below. Draw it on this plate.

potatoes
burger
hard boiled eggs
brown bread
salad
fried egg
chips

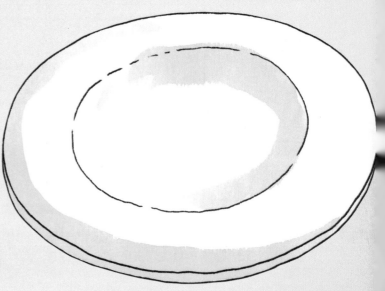

Challenge 3 Medicine can make you better when you are poorly, but i can be dangerous if you do not use it wisely! Write down three rules to remember to stay safe.

1 _____

2 _____

3 _____

Challenge 4 Can you remember the special jobs done by each part of a flowering plant? Write the names of the parts on the labels, then join them to the jobs each part does with a line.

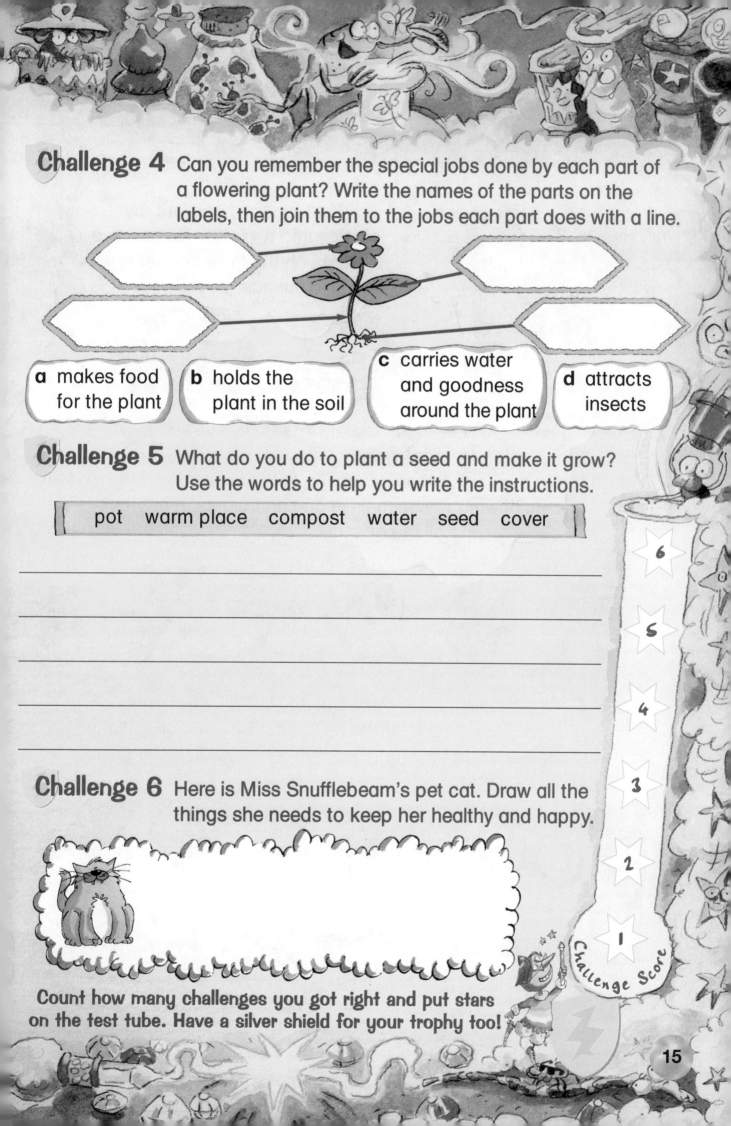

a makes food for the plant

b holds the plant in the soil

c carries water and goodness around the plant

d attracts insects

Challenge 5 What do you do to plant a seed and make it grow? Use the words to help you write the instructions.

| pot | warm place | compost | water | seed | cover |

_____

_____

_____

_____

_____

Challenge 6 Here is Miss Snufflebeam's pet cat. Draw all the things she needs to keep her healthy and happy.

6

5

4

3

2

1

Challenge Score

Count how many challenges you got right and put stars on the test tube. Have a silver shield for your trophy too!

Super Sorting

I am trying to sort out my comics into two sets. Some have plants on the front and others have animals on the cover.

Task 1 Oh dear, this is hard! Can you help me sort my toys into two sets? I want toy animals in one and plants in another. Draw a circle around all the animals.

a   b   c   d   e   f

Task 2 Oops! I bumped into the bat cage and all the bats flew out. Then I knocked over the newt box! Help me find all the animals that have crawled into the garden. Draw a circle around them.

Task 3 Thank you for helping me. Now, just to get things straight, help me to write **animal** or **plant** on these pictures.

a

b

c

d

e

f

g

Sorcerer's Skill Check

Just one more muddle to sort out, then we have finished!
Look at the things on this list. Are they plants or animals?

a cow

b dog

c tree

d fish

e grass

Slurp! You will soon be as smart as Pointy.
Award yourself a silver shield!

Magic Materials

Burp! Have you ever thought about what materials things are made from? Wizard Whimstaff told us about natural materials, like feathers, stone and hay, that are found in nature. Then he also told us about things that are made by people, like plastic and glass.

feathers
hay
stone

natural

plastic
glass

made by people

Task 1

We feel sleepy just looking at this! Think carefully about which of these things are natural and which are made by people. Then draw a circle around the natural things.

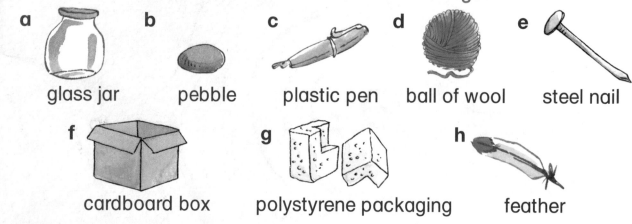

a glass jar **b** pebble **c** plastic pen **d** ball of wool **e** steel nail

f cardboard box **g** polystyrene packaging **h** feather

Task 2

Draw a circle around the materials that have been made by people

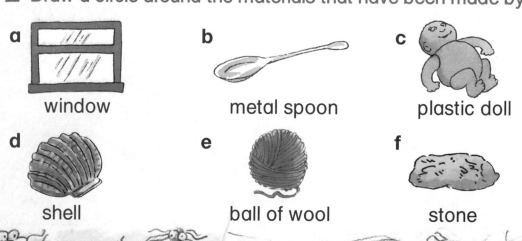

a window **b** metal spoon **c** plastic doll

d shell **e** ball of wool **f** stone

Task 3 Slurp! Can you match the material to where it comes from? Wool comes from sheep, so the ball of wool is joined to the sheep. Try the rest!

a
ball of wool

b
pillow

c
paving slab

d
wooden chair

e
cup

feathers

lump of clay

ball of wool

stone

tree

Sorcerer's Skill Check

Brain cell alert! Time to do some hard thinking! Draw three things in each box.

natural

made by people

Abracadabra! You are learning fast!
Award yourself a silver shield.

Powerful Properties

Wizard Whimstaff has let me do some cooking! I am making bat ice lollies, maggot crispies and slug soup. Yum! Pointy keeps lifting lids and commenting on my recipes. He says the things I am cooking are solids, liquids and gases, but he keeps changing his mind. I am confused!

 solid

 liquid

 gas

Task 1 Oh dear, what a muddle. Can you sort these things into solid, liquid or gas? Write **S**, **L** or **G** on the stars.

a

b

c

d

e

f

Task 2 You are clever! When I made the maggot crispies, I used chocolate. As I warmed it up, it melted and became a liquid. I put the mixture in the fridge and it became a solid again. Read my recipe for slug soup. Add the words **solid**, **liquid** or **gas** to describe each stage.

Chop lots of vegetables (_____) and put them in the cauldron. Add some runny slug slime (_____) and some water (_____). When the cauldron starts to steam (_____), add a pinch of powdered spider (_____).

Task 3 Read my description of making bat ice lollies. Then help me by writing **solid**, **liquid** or **gas** in each box to describe the word that comes before it.

I chopped up some fruit [____] and put it into my bat-shaped moulds. Then I got some orange juice [____] and some lemonade [____], and mixed them together. The bubbles [____] popped on my paws! I poured the mixture into the moulds and put them in the freezer. I made a cup of steaming dragon brew while I was waiting. The steam [____] smelled delicious! When I got the lollies back out of the freezer, they were frozen [____]!

Sorcerer's Skill Check

Just to check you remember everything, look at these pictures and decide whether the things circled in red are solid, liquid or gas. Write **S**, **L** or **G**.

a   b   c   d   e   f

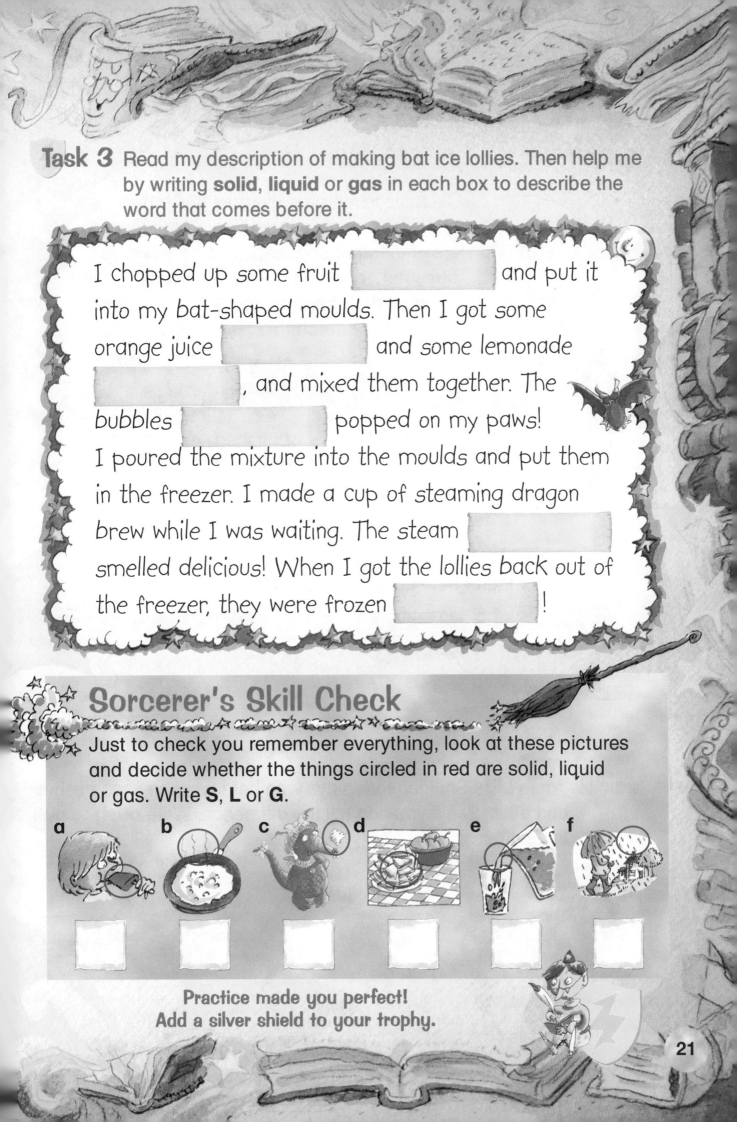

[ ]   [ ]   [ ]   [ ]   [ ]   [ ]

Practice made you perfect!
Add a silver shield to your trophy.

Pushing and Pulling

I have invented supergoo! It is a new, stretchy, green goo that can be made into lots of different shapes. It can be stretched, squashed or bent. It is great fun! Now, when you squash or bend things, you use a push. When you stretch things, you use a pull.

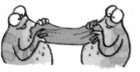
stretched with a pull

squashed with a push

bent with a push

Task 1 Draw a circle around the things that can be squashed, stretched or bent easily. Hey presto!

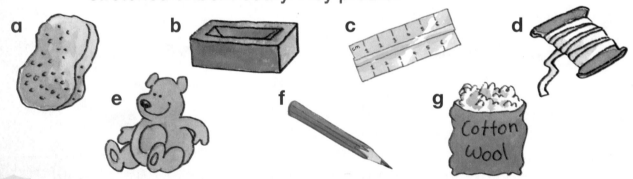

a b c d

e f g Cotton Wool

Task 2 When Miss Snufflebeam plays with her toys, she uses pushes and pulls! See if you can tell the difference. Write **push** or **pull** in the boxes.

a b c

22

Task 3 I have made some models out of supergoo. I want to make some more, but I have run out of goo! Tick (✔) the things from my list I could squash, bend or stretch to make models.

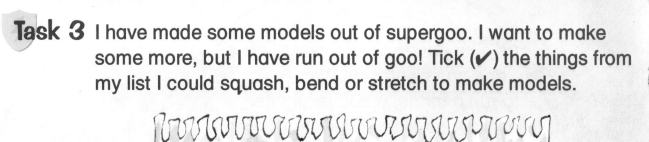

1. plasticine
2. stone
3. modelling clay
4. dough
5. marzipan
6. wood

Sorcerer's Skill Check

Check your knowledge with my true or false quiz! Write **T** for true and **F** for false. Allakazan!

a An iron bar can be bent easily.

b You can change the shape of clay with a push.

c Sponge can be squashed easily.

d When you write, you push the pencil with your hand.

e Elastic is stretchy.

**I'm sure I would have got that muddled up!
You deserve a silver shield.**

Eerie Electricity

Our cave is very modern and has **electricity**! We use it to run a **fridge**, a **cooker**, **lights**, **television** and even a new **computer**! We also have **electric heaters**. Miss Snufflebeam has a battery-operated bat that flies around, so that uses electricity too!

Task 1 Look at the pictures. Which of these things use electricity? Draw a circle around the ones you choose.

Task 2 Super! Now, which of these things use electricity to give us light? Draw a circle around the ones you choose.

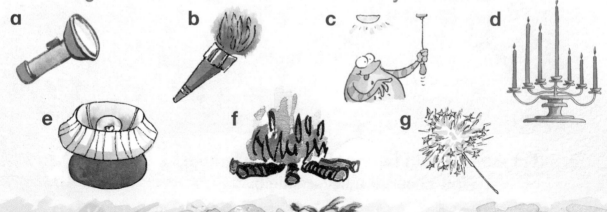

Task 3 Which of these things uses electricity to make a sound? Draw a circle around the ones you choose. It is easy when you know how!

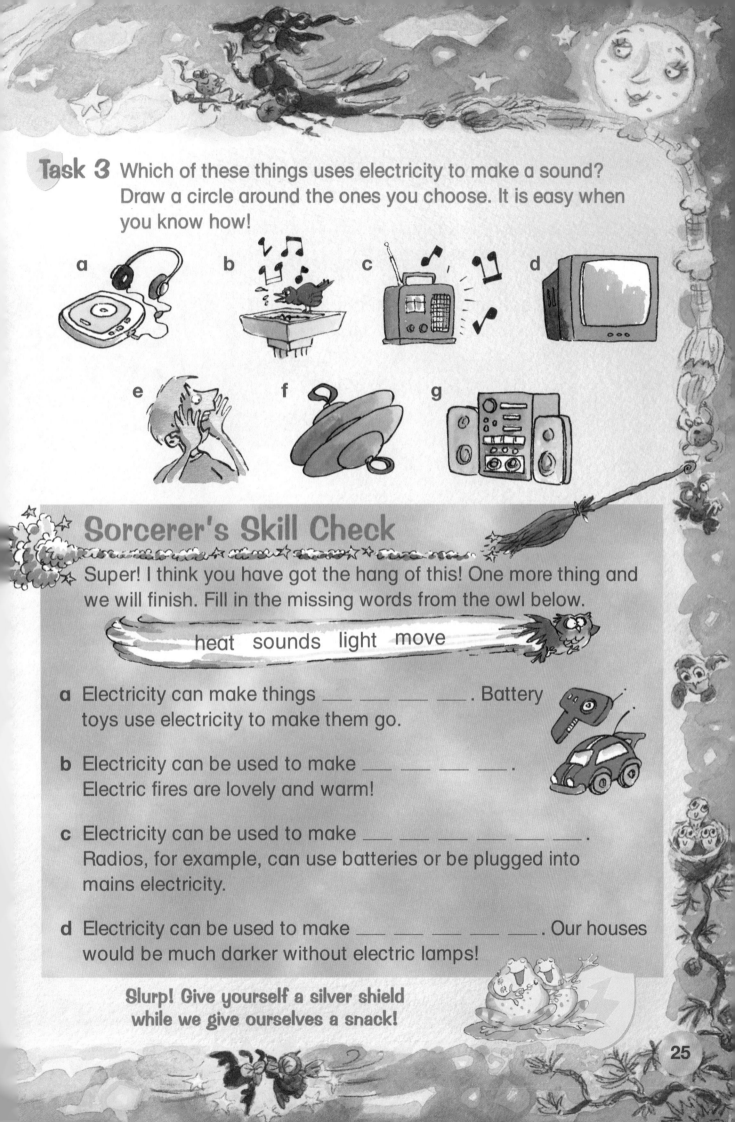

a

b

c

d

e

f

g

Sorcerer's Skill Check

Super! I think you have got the hang of this! One more thing and we will finish. Fill in the missing words from the owl below.

heat   sounds   light   move

a Electricity can make things __ __ __ __ . Battery toys use electricity to make them go.

b Electricity can be used to make __ __ __ __ . Electric fires are lovely and warm!

c Electricity can be used to make __ __ __ __ __ __ . Radios, for example, can use batteries or be plugged into mains electricity.

d Electricity can be used to make __ __ __ __ __ . Our houses would be much darker without electric lamps!

Slurp! Give yourself a silver shield
while we give ourselves a snack!

Creepy Circuits

We have sneaked into Wizard Whimstaff's spell workshop. He has left lots of great stuff lying about! **Bulbs, wires, switches** and **batteries** are all great fun! He left instructions on how to make a **circuit**.

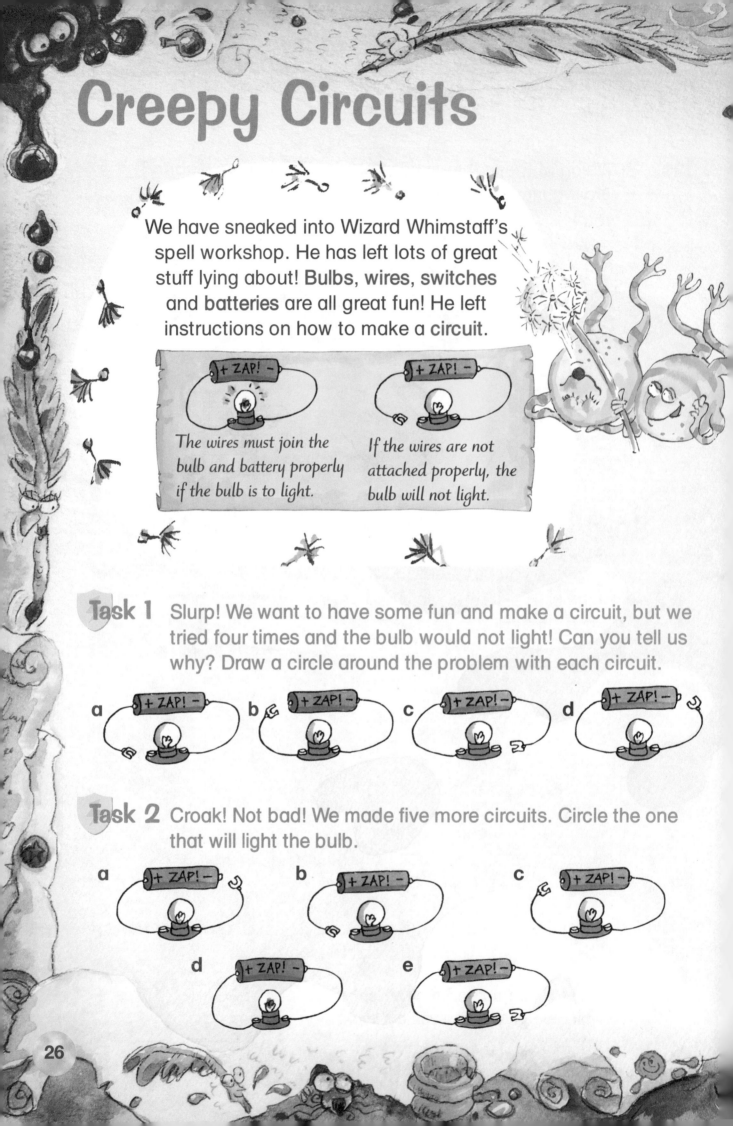

The wires must join the bulb and battery properly if the bulb is to light.

If the wires are not attached properly, the bulb will not light.

Task 1 Slurp! We want to have some fun and make a circuit, but we tried four times and the bulb would not light! Can you tell us why? Draw a circle around the problem with each circuit.

a   b   c   d

Task 2 Croak! Not bad! We made five more circuits. Circle the one that will light the bulb.

a   b   c

d   e

Task 3 Time for another snooze! Answer these questions for us while we have a rest. True or false? Put a **T** for true and **F** for false.

a If there is no battery in a circuit, it will light a bulb.

b All wires need to be joined together correctly to make a battery light a bulb.

c It doesn't matter if some wires are not joined up correctly – the bulb will still light up!

d If the wires are not attached properly, the bulb will not light.

e The battery needs to be joined to the bulb with wires for the bulb to light.

f If the wires are attached properly, the bulb will not light.

Sorcerer's Skill Check

Brain cell alert! Draw a plan of a circuit that will light a bulb for us, so we can remember to do it properly. Do not forget that the wires must all be joined up in the right places!

Oh, you are clever! Take another silver shield!

Apprentice Wizard Challenge 2

Challenge 1   Animal or plant? Draw a circle around the plants.

Challenge 2   Natural or made by people? Draw a circle around the natural things.

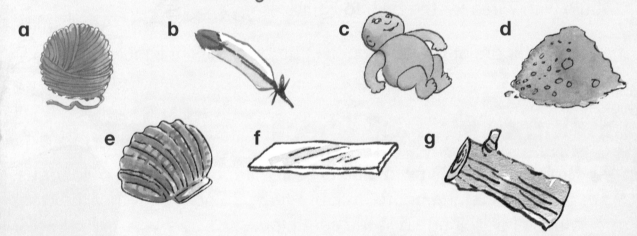

Challenge 3   Solid, liquid or gas? Look at the things circled in red. Write **S** for solid, **L** for liquid or **G** for gas.

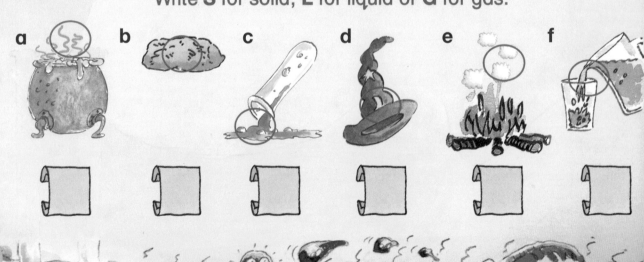

Challenge 4 Draw a circle around the things that can be squashed, stretched or bent easily.

a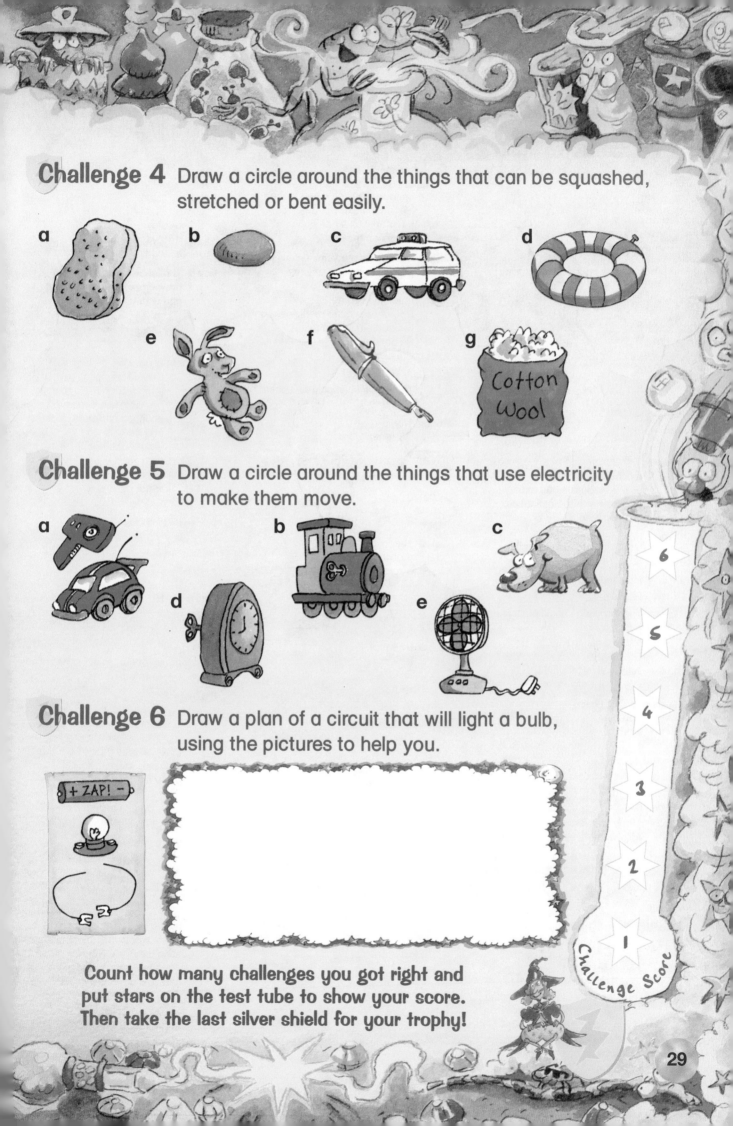

b

c

d

e

f

g

Cotton Wool

Challenge 5 Draw a circle around the things that use electricity to make them move.

a

b

c

d

e

Challenge 6 Draw a plan of a circuit that will light a bulb, using the pictures to help you.

+ ZAP! −

Count how many challenges you got right and put stars on the test tube to show your score. Then take the last silver shield for your trophy!

6

5

4

3

2

1

Challenge Score

Answers

Pages 2–3

Task 1 b c d e a

Task 2 b c e d a

Task 3 **a** 6
      b 3
      c 5
      d 2
      e 1
      f 7
      g 8
      h 4

Sorcerer's Skill Check
    a F
    b T
    c F
    d T
    e T
    f F

Pages 4–5

Task 1 **a** cheese omelette
      b baked potato and beans
      c pasta with tomato sauce
      d egg salad sandwich

Task 2 banana, apple, yoghurt, juice
and sandwich are the healthiest
things; other items may be
included and the lunch may still
be considered healthy

Task 3 The following should be crossed
out:
    eat bags and bags of sweets
    lie about in front of the TV all day
    stay up late every night
    only drink fizzy lemonade

Sorcerer's Skill Check
    a T
    b F
    c T
    d F
    e F
    f F

Pages 6–7

Task 1 Many answers are possible. The
following are example drawings:

Task 2 Silly Sally had a bad headache.
She went into the bathroom
and <u>opened the medicine
cupboard. She took out a bottle
of medicine</u> she had seen her
mum use. Just then, Mum came
into the bathroom. 'Put that
down, Sally!' said Mum. 'Children
must not help themselves to
medicine. It can be very
dangerous!' <u>Sally asked her mum</u>

<u>to give her lots of medicine</u>
because she had a headache.
Her mum said 'No, silly! You
must only take one spoonful, like
it says on the bottle.'

Task 3 Never take medicine unless a
grown-up gives it to you.
Never take things from the
medicine cabinet.
Do not take more medicine than
the bottle tells you to.
Be careful because pills can look
like sweets!

Sorcerer's Skill Check
The following should be ticked:
a c d e f

Pages 8–9

Task 1

Task 2 The following are example
drawings:

Task 3 **a** carrot
      b lettuce
      c apple
      d rose
      e celery

Sorcerer's Skill Check
The following is an example
drawing:

Pages 10–11

Task 1 d a c b

Task 2 b d c a

Task 3 Many answers are possible. The
following are example drawings:

Sorcerer's Skill Check
The following sentences should
be ticked:
b and c

Pages 12–13

Task 1 **a** clean
      b water
      c play
      d toys
      e food

Task 2 The following are example
drawings of toys, food, hay
and water:

Task 3 Many answers are possible.
 play: Rizzo needs toys to
play with.
 bed: Her bed needs to be
changed and kept clean
and dry.
food: Rizzo needs fresh,
tasty food every day.
water: Rizzo needs clean
water every day.

Sorcerer's Skill Check
    a F
    b F
    c T
    d T

Pages 14–15

Challenge 1
    b c d e a

Challenge 2
    brown bread, salad, hard boiled
    eggs, potatoes

Challenge 3
    Any three from the following:
    1. Never take medicine unless
    a grown-up gives it to you.
    2. Never take things from the
    medicine cabinet.
    3. Do not take more medicine
    than the bottle tells you to.
    4. Be careful because pills can
    look like sweets!

Challenge 4

    leaf: **a** makes food for the plant
    roots: **b** holds the plant in the soil
    stem: **c** carries water and
    goodness around the plant
    flower: **d** attracts insects

Challenge 5
    Put compost in a pot.
    Put the seed in the pot and cover
    it with compost.
    Water the seed.
    Put the pot in a warm place.

Challenge 6

Many answers are possible. The following are example drawings:

Pages 16–17

Task 1

Task 2

Task 3
- **a** plant
- **b** plant
- **c** animal
- **d** animal
- **e** plant
- **f** animal
- **g** animal

Sorcerer's Skill Check
- **a** animal
- **b** animal
- **c** plant
- **d** animal
- **e** plant

Pages 18–19

Task 1

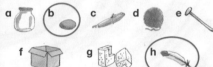

Task 2

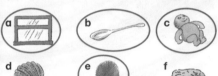

Task 3
- **a** sheep
- **b** feathers
- **c** stone
- **d** tree
- **e** lump of clay

Sorcerer's Skill Check
Many answers are possible. The following are example drawings:

natural

made by people

Pages 20–21

Task 1
- **a** S
- **b** L
- **c** G
- **d** S
- **e** L
- **f** G

Task 2
Chop lots of vegetables (<u>solid</u>) and put them in the cauldron. Add some runny slug slime (<u>liquid</u>) and some water (<u>liquid</u>). When the cauldron starts to steam (<u>gas</u>), add a pinch of powdered spider (<u>solid</u>).

Task 3
solid, liquid, liquid, gas, gas, solid

Sorcerer's Skill Check
- **a** S
- **b** G
- **c** G
- **d** S
- **e** L
- **f** L

Pages 22–23

Task 1

Task 2
- **a** push
- **b** pull
- **c** push

Task 3
The following should be ticked:
1 3 4 5

Sorcerer's Skill Check
- **a** F
- **b** T
- **c** T
- **d** T
- **e** T

Pages 24–25

Task 1

Task 2

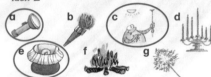

Task 3

Sorcerer's Skill Check
- **a** move
- **b** heat
- **c** sounds
- **d** light

Pages 26–27

Task 1

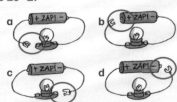

Task 2

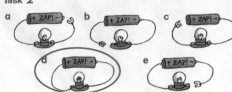

Task 3
- **a** F
- **b** T
- **c** F
- **d** T
- **e** T
- **f** F

Sorcerer's Skill Check
The following is an example drawing:

Pages 28–29

Challenge 1

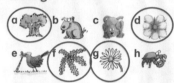

Challenge 2

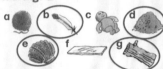

Challenge 3
- **a** G
- **b** S
- **c** L
- **d** S
- **e** G
- **f** L

Challenge 4

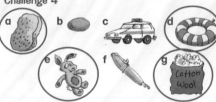

Challenge 5

Challenge 6
The following is an example drawing:

The end

Wizard's Trophy of Excellence

Great
Growing

Fantastic
Food

Mighty
Medicine

Potty
Plants

Seed
Sorcery

Playful
Pets

Super
Sorting

Magic
Materials

Powerful
Properties

Pushing
and Pulling

Eerie
Electricity

Creepy
Circuits

Apprentice Wizard
Challenge 1

Apprentice Wizard
Challenge 2

This is to state that Wizard Whimstaff awards

Apprentice _____

the Trophy of Science Wizardry. Congratulations!

Published 2003
10 9 8 7 6 5 4

Letts Educational, The Chiswick Centre,
414 Chiswick High Road, London W4 5TF
Tel 020 8996 3333   Fax 020 8742 8390
Email mail@lettsed.co.uk
www.letts-education.com

Text, design and illustrations © Letts Educational Ltd 2003

Author: Lynn Huggins-Cooper
Book Concept and Development:
Helen Jacobs, Publishing Director; Sophie London, Project Editor
Design: Linda Males
Editor: Andrew Schofield
Illustrations: Mike Phillips (Beehive illustration)
Cover Illustration: Neil Chapman (Beehive illustration)

Letts Educational Limited is a division of Granada Learning Limited.
Part of Granada plc.

British Library Cataloguing in Publication Data

A CIP record for this book is available from the British Library.

ISBN 1 84315 130 8

Printed in Italy

Colour reproduction by PDQ Repro Limited, Bungay, Suffolk.